TWO-MINUTE
➤ STORIES ➤

TWO-MINUTE STORIES

AS TOLD BY

CARL S. PATTON

TO
BOYS AND GIRLS
WHO LISTENED AND
CAME BACK FOR
MORE

WILLETT, CLARK & COLBY
440 SOUTH DEARBORN STREET, CHICAGO
200 FIFTH AVENUE, NEW YORK

1930

CONTENTS

TWO-MINUTE
STORIES

HIS FIRST HAT
AND HIS LAST NAME

◆ ◆

One of the best stories that was ever written is the life story of the colored man, Booker Washington, written by himself. In this story he tells about his first hat and his last name.

Up to the time he went to school, Booker had never worn a hat. He had never noticed that boys generally wore hats, and he had never felt the need of one himself. But when he went to school, all the other boys had hats.

He went home and told his mother about it. She said she had no money to buy him a hat. But she bought a piece of heavy cloth, cut it into two strips, and sewed the two together in such shape that it would stay on his head. So the hat business was soon settled. Booker Washington used to say in later years that of all the hats he ever owned, the only one that really gave him pleasure was this first one.

The name business was settled even more quickly and easily than the hat business. Before he went to school, his name had been just Booker. He never knew where he got even that much. He did not know that people generally had two names. One had always been enough for him. But as he sat there in the schoolroom the first day and the teacher was asking one boy after another for his name, Booker noticed that every boy gave two names.

Booker could not go home to ask his mother about this. So he made up his mind that when it came his turn to give his name, he would have a last name — and he spoke it right up — " Booker Washington." Nobody asked him where he got this last name, and he kept it as long as he lived.

These two simple incidents are parts of a great story of how a boy — who, till the time he went to school, did not know that anybody wore a hat or had two names — grew into one of the great leaders of a race. His death was noted the world over and spoken of in almost every paper of the North and the South as a loss to the whole country.

Makes us ashamed, doesn't it, that with all our opportunities, we make so little of them? Perhaps we have too many of them, and have them too easily. Well, you can't help it if you do start life with a hat and a name already made for you. But there is one thing you can do. You can see to it that there is something under the hat and that the name grows more honorable because you wear it.

THE GIRL
AND THE PAGEANT

Thinking of the pageants that have become popular in many parts of the country reminds me of a story about one. There was a young woman who was interested in the early history of various towns in the Middle West — especially in stories of the Indians and the pioneers.

By an article she wrote for one of the magazines, she became known to a committee who had to arrange a great historical pageant in their city. They asked her to come and learn what she could about their early history and see whether she could make a pageant for them out of it.

When the time for the pageant came, she had hundreds of children and grown folks, some dressed as Indians, some as Mexicans, some as pioneers with their ponies and their rifles, all ready for the great show. There were Indian camp-fires, and raids, and battles in the pageant, and shouting and shooting and lots of paint and feathers. It was given in a great open-air amphitheater, on a stage that would hold hundreds of people. Woven into it, was the history of the city, from the time it was an Indian trading-fort down to the present moment — all gathered and written and put into the play by this girl.

As the pageant went on, the audience became more and more enthusiastic, until finally they began to call for the author. The author was behind the stage. She had helped pretty nearly every boy in the performance to get his war paint on right, and every girl to fix her Indian blanket so it wouldn't come off, and she did not notice what the audience was doing. But the other people back of the stage understood that the audience was calling for her, and without saying a word to her, before she had time to object, they pushed her upon the stage.

She had on a big blue apron. Her hair was tumbled about her eyes. On her face was Indian paint and every other kind; and just at that moment, as luck would have it, her mouth was full of pins. And there, all of a sudden, before she knew what had happened, she found herself facing an audience of ten thousand people. She put her hand up to push her hair out of her eyes. Then it came over her — where she was and what she looked like — and she grabbed her big apron and threw it up over her face. Then the audience rose, like one man, and cheered until they were hoarse.

I suppose that if this girl had come on the stage in evening dress, looking as if she were there for the purpose of being honored, the people would have been polite to her, but they would not have gone wild about her. But that paint, that apron, and those pins showed that she hadn't expected anything, and wasn't thinking of anything, except to make her show go as it ought to. The greatest honor that can come to any of us is to have deserved an honor and not to have been looking for it.

THE
JACK-KNIFE

People get great satisfaction sometimes out of small things. I know one man who gets a great deal out of a jack-knife. Not out of one particular jack-knife, but just out of a jack-knife in general. He has a good many of them. Some of them have been given him by friends, and he treasures them on that account.

He has knives that were made in England, and knives that were made in Germany, and knives that were made in Connecticut, one knife that was made in France and one that was made in Japan. Some of them are expensive; some of them are cheap. They are smaller and larger, sharper and duller, better and worse. Some have one blade; some have three; and one of them has four blades and a corkscrew and a pair of scissors in it.

But this man gets great comfort out of his knives. He is somehow sort of dependent upon them. He can't get along without them. I have known him, more than once, to get started down town and to discover that he hadn't a knife with him and go back a block, or even get off one car and take another car back, to get one of his knives. Not that he had any need for it on that occasion. He might be going to church, or to a party. But he has told me that he somehow feels that if he has a jack-knife with him, he is prepared for anything that may happen; and if he hasn't it, he feels as if he might not get through the day. He wants it, not to cut something with, but for the comfort of having it with him.

I have known him, when something has happened to disturb him, to lay out his whole stock of knives, put the best one into his pocket and start out quite relieved. I have even known him, when he had a fit of the blues, to go into a hardware store and take half an hour looking over the stock of knives. He would finally buy one. Then he would go down town on the street car with his hand clutching the new knife in his pocket and his peace of mind quite restored.

Curious, isn't it? Curious and interesting. I don't know how it is, but many people are made in such a way that they can get great satisfaction out of small and trivial things. I hope it is so with you. In your case it may not be a jack-knife, but I hope it will always be something.

THE WOMAN
WHO GOT ELECTED

Coming home on the boat from Europe one summer, I made the acquaintance of a woman who had recently been elected. It was before the day of " votes for women," but this woman didn't stop for that. It happened this way.

She had been a teacher for fifty years in the public schools of Rochester, New York. All that time she had not had much chance to see the world; for though she was not married, she had adopted a family of four children.

First she took one; but she had heard that an only child was sure to be spoiled, so she took another. These were both girls, and she thought she ought to have a boy to be a brother to them; and then she thought this boy would be lonesome without a brother, so she took a fourth. Besides teaching school all day, she had to be father and mother and housekeeper to all these children. She did not have much chance to get away.

A newspaper offered prizes to people who got the largest number of votes in the form of coupons cut from the paper. One prize was an automobile, another was a piano, and another was a trip to Europe. When you have taught a grade school for fifty years and have brought up four children on your wages, you are apt to be poorer when you get through than when you began. That was this woman's condition. So when somebody said to her, " You ought to try for that European trip," an old hope, cherished for many years and then for many years given up, came back to her.

But she did not believe she could be elected. Some of the people who had gone in for the prizes would buy votes; she could not do that. Some of them were pretty girls; she could not compete with them. But her friends persuaded her to let it be known that she wanted votes, and so she did.

The votes began to come in from all over New York state and apparently from everywhere else. People she remembered but hadn't seen for thirty years; boys who had worried her in school and had ever since been looking for a chance to make it up to her; sons and daughters, and nieces and nephews, and friends and neighbors of her old pupils for fifty years back, all worked for her. Other people heard who she was, saw how she was running, and sent in their votes. Until finally, when the votes were all in, how close do you think she came to being beaten? I will tell you. She had just two million votes more than she needed.

Nobody who went to Europe that summer

9

had a better time than this old lady. For wherever she went, she saw not only the cathedrals and the galleries and the cities, but in the background that great sea of faces — all beautiful to her — of the people who had helped her to this great happiness because they liked her.

You may never have this same kind of chance to find out how many people remember you kindly. But you may make up your mind to one thing; you will never do much good in the world and you will never have much fun in it, unless people like you.

THE BIG MAN
AND THE LITTLE ONE

William James was one of the great men of
this country. People crowded to hear him talk.
Students patterned their writing and their
thinking after him. Books about him, or dedicated to him, or showing the admiration of their
writers for him or his influence upon them,
appear every day and probably will for many
years. He really was a great man.

Now one way you can tell a great man is by
the way he acts toward a little one. When Mr.
James was a professor at Harvard, a freshman
was standing one day in front of a book store.
There were some books in the window, and
among them a volume of O. Henry's stories.
Another man came up whom the freshman did
not know. "Have you read the new one?"
asked the other man. "No," answered the
freshman. "Neither have I," said the other
man, "but I have read all the others." "He's
great, though — don't you think so?" asked
the freshman. "Grand," replied the other
man. "Let's go in and buy this one." So
they did.

Coming out of the store the other man said
to the freshman, "You'd better come home to
dinner with me; my folks are away and I'm all

alone tonight." He did not ask the freshman's name, and the young man took him for some instructor.

They went to the other man's house, a big house on a quiet street with plenty of easy chairs and lots of books. After dinner they sat around and talked — about football, about the big men among the students, about the things the students liked and didn't like, about fraternities, college clubs, comic operas, and why one man was popular and another man was not. The freshman got the impression that the other man was about his own age.

Finally, at eleven o'clock, the freshman started to go home. As he stood in the doorway telling the other man what a good time he had had, the other man said to him, " You must come again, and we'll have another talk." Then he added, " I don't think I know your name." The freshman told him, and said, " And now may I ask yours? " "William James," replied the other man.

There are plenty of men who will make you afraid of them because they think they are big, or because they try to make you think so. But when you meet a really big man, you need never be afraid of him.

THE
BIRTHDAY PARADE

I read the other day about a girl who was born in Montreal on the 17th of March. It was a Catholic city, and full of Irish people. But this girl's mother was a Protestant and an American.

The girl always had a glorious time on her birthday. Her mother was poor and could not give her presents or a party. But she didn't miss these pleasures. For every time her birthday came around, somebody — she supposed it was Santa Claus — arranged a big parade for her.

There were men on horseback and women in carriages. There were bands; people sang and marched; and everybody wore a sprig of green, which was her favorite color. She wondered how they knew it. But such things get around; and Santa Claus and other people of that sort know everything. It was certainly a great birthday.

Until she was eight years old, this little girl never suspected that this parade was for anybody but her. It always came to her house. It usually stopped there. The fact that the house was in the main street, and that the city hall was across the road from it, didn't matter.

People in the procession always smiled at her. She just naturally thought it was all for her.

Then somebody discovered that she thought this and told her that the party was not for her, but for St. Patrick! Of this St. Patrick she had never heard. It seemed that he had not been born in Montreal and that he had been dead for a long time. Why should anybody march for him?

So this little girl came to a wise conclusion. Instead of being disappointed that the procession was not intended for her, she would continue to think that it *was*. And always, on St. Patrick's day, when the bits of green were everywhere and the bands began to play, she just enjoyed it exactly as she used to and counted it her party.

And she was right. For all things in this world are for the people who can enjoy them. One man may own the fences and the dirt, but another man can enjoy the color in the sky above them. When a mocking bird sings in the back yard, it makes no difference whether it is the neighbor's back yard or yours; the song is for you if you stop to listen and enjoy it. When you saw "Peter Pan" or "The Blue Bird," didn't it seem to you as if the authors had written these plays and the players were playing them expressly for you?

14

All the artists, and all the creators, including God, produce all the beauty and the loveliness of the world for the particular benefit of whoever can enjoy it. The whole world is yours.

THE
WALL-PAPER

When the great novelist, William Dean Howells, was a boy eight or nine years old, his father went to live in an out-of-the-way place in Ohio. The only house he could find was an old log cabin. He and the boys mended the floors and the shingles after a fashion. They put glass in the windows. When everything else was fixed, they needed some wall-paper. But there was none to be had. And the family had no money to buy it with, even if it could have been bought.

At the old abandoned post office there was a barrel of newspapers. They had been sent to subscribers who refused to take them from the office because they did not want to pay for them. So they were fresh and clean. The father and the boys took these newspapers and papered the cabin with them.

I suppose they were not so very pretty. But they did have one advantage. There was a continued story in them. There were no books in the cabin. But at night, when the work was done, you could take a candle, climb up on a chair and read this story. You might find the first chapter in the top left-hand corner of the kitchen, and the second chapter in the middle of the sitting-room wall.

The boys found one chapter after another, until — just as it got to the most exciting point, and they were about to discover who had stolen the diamonds — the story disappeared. They searched high and low on the walls, they went back to the barrel. Not another word could they find. The end of the story was probably on the back of the kitchen paper!

This little experience shows us two things. First, we all want things to look right; we want something to cover up the cracks of life and make it smooth and clean. Nobody wants to live in an ugly world. But also nobody wants to live in an uninteresting world, where there is nothing to get excited about. We want wall-paper. But we want stories even more.

The boy who had this experience became one of America's greatest story writers. He was so great that, though he had never been to college himself, Harvard and Yale and half a dozen other universities offered him professor-ships. But he preferred just to write stories. Who knows but the thing that got him started was the lost end of the story on the wall-paper?

BEATEN
AT HIS OWN GAME

I knew a boy a few years ago who was a great trial to his teacher. To begin with, he would not study. And to end with, he would do everything else. But he had a teacher who was too much for him. She was too much for him, not because she was too big for him, or too strong for him, but because she was too wise for him. And this is how he learned it.

He came into the schoolroom one morning, singing. It was nothing bad that he was sing-ing — it seems to me it was " Onward Christian Soldiers." And he wasn't singing very loud — under his breath, but still loud enough for everyone in the room to hear him. Across the floor he shuffled, singing, and sat down at his desk. He took out his books and opened them, still singing.

Most teachers, I suppose, would have said, " Robert," which was what he expected and hoped for. Some teachers probably would have gone over to his seat and jerked him out of it — and would have looked very absurd in the process — and that would have suited Robert very well too. Some perhaps would have ended by thrashing him; and would have been very much ashamed of themselves afterwards.

But what do you think this teacher did to him? She "didn't do a thing." She did not speak to him; and even when he looked up at her she was always careful to be looking the other way. She went quietly up and down the aisles and said to the others, "Now don't pay any attention to Robert." She omitted the opening exercises, so that Robert could have a better chance to sing. She omitted the first class.

Robert was surprised and disappointed and did not know what to do. But there was only one thing he could do. He had to sing! He got red in the face, but he had to keep on. He got short of breath, but he could not stop. He knew he was beaten, but to quit singing would be to confess it. So he sang. And the longer he sang the more he wanted to stop, but the more he couldn't. He hoped something would happen, but nothing did. If the teacher would only have told him to sing, he could have stopped. But she just let him alone.

And so he sang and sang and sang, until it was time for recess. The teacher looked at him, to see whether or not she should make him sing the rest of the forenoon. But he did look so foolish and so uncomfortable that she took pity on him, and dismissed the school for recess. And when they all came back, Robert was a model boy. . . . This was three or four years ago. No word ever passed between Robert and his teacher on this musical performance. But he has been a model boy ever since.

When we are beaten at our own game, we usually have sense enough to see what it means. It is a good thing, in school or out of it, not to start anything that is likely to come back like a boomerang upon your own head.

THE
LOCKET

A lady whom I met down East last summer told me a story that impressed me much. It was a story about her father and mother — especially about her mother. They were Norwegians. When her father was a young man, he came to America against the wishes of his family. They predicted that nothing good would come of such a move.

But there was a girl in that same town in Norway, with whom the young man had talked over the future. And as girls will sometimes do, she had made this young man a promise. He was to go to America and get work and save his money. When he had enough money, he was to send for her, and she was to come and they would be married.

He came to America. But he had a long hard time getting started. Work was scarce; men were plenty; nobody seemed to need him. The prospects of the girl in Norway did not look good. Finally the young man got a job with a maker of telescopes and other scientific instruments. He lived in a little room over the shop and he boarded himself.

At the end of the first month, when he drew his first wages, he did not put them into the bank for the great event; he didn't buy something better to wear or to eat, as he might well have done. He spent the whole month's wages for a locket, and sent it to the girl in Norway.

Then he saved his money, and by and by the girl came. The man was promoted. He was made a partner in the business, and finally its owner. He became well known among scientific and scholarly men. He made telescopes for the Lick observatory, and for the Lowell observatory at Flagstaff. I suppose he made more fine and large telescopes than any other man in America.

He grew rich. He went everywhere to see and talk with scientific men. Although he had never been to college, Amherst — and perhaps one more college — conferred a degree upon him. His wife went everywhere with him and shared in all his prosperity.

After he died at a good old age, his wife brought out the locket he had sent her before she came to America, and began to wear it again. Then she grew old and feeble and finally childish. Her daughter told me that when she got to where she could not remember her own daughter's name, or much of anything else out of her long and happy life, there was one thing she never forgot. That was the locket. Every day she wore it. Every night when her daughter helped her into bed, she said in the same words, as if she had not said it before, "This is the locket your father gave me. He bought it with the first money he ever earned. Put it right there." And the next night, and the next, and always, "This is the locket your father gave me. He bought it with the first money he ever earned. Put it right there."

There is a thing in the world that we call love. Sometimes it is the love of a man for his wife, sometimes of a mother for her children, sometimes of a boy for his chum — but whatever kind it is, it is the finest thing, absolutely the finest thing, in the world. Keep hold of it.

THE BOY
AND THE BOOK

◆   ◆

At St. George's Church on the East Side of New York, thirty years ago, they had a library for the people of the neighborhood. It was a very poor neighborhood, and the public libraries were not yet scattered all over town. Therefore people were very glad to get the books from St. George's.

Many children came in to get books. They were free if you didn't keep them overtime. If you did, you got a postal card from the librarian — one of the girls of the neighborhood — telling you how much you owed. There was a boy from a very poor family who drew a book. He didn't have much time to read and he couldn't read very fast when he did have time. So he got a card from the librarian telling him that there was four cents overdue on his book.

It was late in the fall — perhaps November — and the weather was very cold. The boy came in with the book. He had no shoes nor stockings on, and he looked miserable enough. The librarian looked at him. She knew him. And when he handed out his book and his card and said, " I owe four pennies," she was sorry for him. " Well, Charlie," she said, " you can

pay two pennies this week and two next week."
But the little ragged chap replied, " No; I've
got 'em here. I worked for 'em, and what is
four pennies for all I got out of that book? "
The librarian looked at his book; it was
Robinson Crusoe.

It is a great thing to appreciate what we
have. Maybe some of us have too much. Anyway, here was this little chap who hadn't
anything. But sitting in the corner at the
miserable place he called home, he had been
reading his book and sailing the seas with
Robinson Crusoe. I know exactly how excited
he got when he discovered the footprint in the
sand, and how long he looked at the picture of
Friday kneeling down to Robinson. And he
went out and earned his four pennies rather
than give up the book before he was through
with it.

THE WOMAN
AND THE BABY

◆   ◆

One time at the railroad station in Ann Arbor, I saw a beautiful sight. It was a woman with a baby.

Not an ordinary woman nor an ordinary baby. The woman was old enough so that her own children were grown up. The baby was a tiny thing in a multitude of blankets. There were other women with the one who had the baby. She allowed them to open the door and carry the suitcase, but never to handle the bundle of blankets. She opened this bundle for me to look in. She did not seem to be at all bashful about it. " Isn't he glorious? " she said.

The train was late, but she did not care to lay the baby down. When the train came she walked down the platform. I was afraid her hat would fall off — she held her head so high. " Don't I carry him fine? " she asked.

Then she told me how, a few days before, she had come by the baby. " It was born in the hospital," she said, " and my daughter, who is a nurse there, wrote me about it. She said the mother had no home and could not keep the baby, and maybe if I would come I could have it. I came for it, but as I had been delayed in

26

starting, the mother had given me up and had decided to take the baby to Detroit and put it in a foundlings' home. So when I got off my train in Ann Arbor, I saw another woman, with a baby in her arms, getting on the same train.

"Something inside of me told me that was the baby I was after. I ran down the platform and said to the woman, 'Is this the baby?' 'What baby?' asked the other woman. 'Why, the baby I have come for,' said I. Then the other woman called to the brakeman, 'Throw off my satchel.' And she began to cry, and I began to cry, and we all got into a hack and went back to the hospital, and so I got the baby. Isn't he grand?"

As I watched her, I thought of the words of Walt Whitman:

"I see the sleeping babe, nestling the breast of its mother;
Hushed, I study them long and long."

Then I thought of something better than this — I thought of a picture that has been painted by thousands of artists — that hangs in every gallery in Europe, and almost in all the world, and that stands for a love like unto the love of God — the picture of Mary and the Christ-child. I hope the baby may grow up to be a good man and make his new mother

27

glad.   But whatever becomes of him, it is a sign of the coming of the kingdom of God that there are people now and then who understand that the finest thing in the world is humanity, and who will not, if they can help it, allow even a fragment of it to be thrown away or lost.

OH
CLO!

As the poet Coleridge was walking in London one day, he heard a peddler calling out old clothes. The peddler did not say "old clothes." He said, "Oh Clo!" Coleridge, like all poets, was particular about the use of the English language, and it offended him to hear this man say "Oh Clo!"

He listened as long as he could stand it. Then he went up to the peddler and said, "Don't you know that that is not the way to pronounce 'old clothes'? Can't you say 'old clothes' as I do now?" Then he said it over three or four times, very distinctly, for the peddler's instruction.

The peddler looked at him patiently until he had finished his lesson; then said to him, in a perfectly clear pronunciation, "I can say 'old clothes' just as easily as you can. But if you had to say it ten times a minute for an hour at a time, you would say 'Oh Clo!' just as I do."

The peddler was quite right. A man who should try to say "old clothes" perfectly distinctly, at the top of his voice, for an hour at a time, wouldn't have any voice left with which to say it. His throat would be twisted up so tight that no sound would come through it at all. But a man with a respectable voice ought to be able to say " Oh Clo! " all day.

I suppose the poet went through a few imaginary vocal exercises while the peddler was making his reply. Then the peddler moved on down the street calling " Oh Clo! " The poet was so much impressed with his own mistake and with the justice of the peddler's reply that he ran after him and gave him a shilling — the last one he had.

Every man knows his own business. The poet knows his, the peddler his. If the poet should speak like a peddler, everybody would laugh at him. Every man knows his own business. You will be tempted to forget this, many times. You will feel that the editor does not know how to edit, nor the preacher to preach, nor the doctor to doctor, and that you are the only person who knows how to do all these, and many other things, just as they ought to be done.

Not every man knows his business perfectly, of course; or some of us would do ours better than we do. But poorly as he knows it, he knows it better than the folks who stand around and tell him how. Poet, peddler, or whatever you are, know your own trade.

OFFICER
OR MAN?

I read in the paper once a story told by an American woman who lived in France during the war. She said: " The American wounded were being brought in from the second battle of the Marne. A fussy American woman in a khaki uniform and a Sam Brown belt knelt over a stretcher and asked, ' Is this case an officer or only a man? ' The brawny corporal who stood beside the stretcher gave her a grim laugh and said, ' Well, lady, he ain't no officer, but he's been hit twice in the innards; both legs busted; he's got two bullets in both arms; and we dropped him three times without his lettin' out a squeak, so I guess ye can call him a man.' "

This story speaks for itself. But I want to say one word about it, and that is that there is only one way you can really tell a man. Clothes don't mark him for sure. Badges don't. Rank doesn't.

I am reminded of a story about a hard-headed old justice of the peace. There came to him one day a man who didn't amount to much but who had been appointed to some political office — postmaster or something of that sort. " I want you to qualify me for office," he said to the justice. " I'll swear you in if that's what you want," replied the justice, " but God Almighty couldn't qualify you."

Nothing put upon the outside of you — no judge's gown, no doctor's hood, no anything that anyone can pin on you or put around your shoulders — can make you a man. The one last touch that is needed for that must come from within yourself. If you " take it like a man," then you are one.

TWO TRIPS
OF AN OLD LADY

◆ ◆

While I was in Palo Alto, I heard part of the story which Dr. Jordan had written about the founding of Leland Stanford University. In all that story, stirring as it was, nothing appealed to me more than the brief account of two trips made by Mrs. Stanford.

Mr. and Mrs. Stanford had agreed to leave all their money to build a university. Just as they were getting it done, Mr. Stanford died. He left Mrs. Stanford responsible for the whole thing. She was a quiet, frail, elderly lady who had never had to be responsible for anything. Then a law-suit came on, to keep her from spending her money on the university.

Here is where the first trip came in. The suit was tried in California, and appealed to Washington. The Supreme Court there was months behind in its work. It would not get to the Stanford case for a year — maybe more. Meantime the profs would starve and probably quit; the students would go home; the university would go to pieces.

Mrs. Stanford just put on her bonnet and went to Washington, where she called on President Cleveland and laid the case before him. President Cleveland got hold of one of the

Supreme Court officials, and had the Stanford case tried and out of the way in a couple of weeks. So the university went on.

Though the other trip did not succeed so well as this one, it was in itself more picturesque and daring. Mrs. Stanford had some jewels her husband had given her from time to time. When the law-suit was over, a panic came on. Mrs. Stanford had a right to sell her land, but nobody would buy land. Also she had her railroads, but nobody would buy railroads. Mrs. Stanford thought of her jewels. But everybody was so hard up you couldn't even sell diamonds.

This was the year of the Queen's Jubilee, in London. There would be a lot of rich people in London. If Mrs. Stanford had her jewels over there she might sell them for what they were worth. To send them by express, pay insurance on them and pay someone to do the business for her would cost a large sum. So she just took an old suitcase, dumped those jewels into it, and she and her maid started with it for London.

They stowed the suitcase under their bed in the sleeper and in their room on the steamer. They put it up into the rack on the English train — five hundred thousand dollars' worth of rubies and diamonds and gold things, in an old suitcase, carried by two unprotected

34

women — with all the thieves and the burglars and the pick-pockets that there are on trains and steamers and city streets. And then they didn't sell the jewels that summer. They carried them back in the same suitcase, and nobody was the wiser or the worse off for the whole trip.

If you should write a thousand pages about the things this lady did for her beloved university, you could not make her bravery, her independence, her self-reliance stand out better than by the mere statement of these two trips she took. Now why should anybody ever be discouraged about the human race, when quiet, elderly ladies have such stuff as this in them?

HE
WAS SCARED

◆   ◆

When Philip Gibbs came to this country from England he was very much scared. He had been all through the war as a newspaper correspondent. He had been in the trenches, and under fire, and out in no-man's-land. But in America he was scared. He was scared first, he says, by the traffic in New York, and he thought he surely would be killed.

But he was most scared when he had to make speeches. "As we drove up to Carnegie Hall," he tells us, "I was cold with fright. My fear increased until I was stiff with it when my brother shook hands with me, patted me on the back as if I were about to go over the top, and pushed me through a little door. I found myself facing a great audience. I was conscious of innumerable faces, white shirt fronts, and eyes — eyes — eyes, staring at me from the great arena of stalls and from the galleries up to the roof. My tongue stuck to the roof of my mouth, my knees weakened."

Then came another terror. "There was a sudden movement," he says, "like a tidal wave, among all those people. It was as if they were all advancing upon me, possibly with intent to kill." Then suddenly it came over him. They

36

were paying him a great honor! They were standing up, not to move down on him and kill him, but just to greet him, and show him how glad they were to see him.

The chairman made an introduction. Sir Philip didn't hear a word of it. He knew now that they weren't going to hurt him, but he was still scared. He got going. Six times he looked at his wrist watch to see if it was time to stop. Then another terror seized him. Probably the watch had stopped, maybe he had spoken an hour too long! He put it to his ear; the great crowd burst into laughter, and then — according to Gibbs — " Some spirit of friendship and good will reached up to me and gave me courage."

This is a sort of parable of what happens to us all in life. We are all scared, often. Scared of the things we have to do, scared of what may happen to us, scared generally and mostly of people. By and by it comes to us that people do not mean us any harm. They are not moving down on us to kill us, but only standing up to be nice to us. The longer I live the more I feel that there isn't much to be afraid of. So take from me this one little piece of advice — *don't be scared.*

FROM
WHICH DIRECTION?

Not so very long ago, I happened to be attending a lecture on chemistry. The lecturer was talking about an experiment he had been conducting and he said that something or other happened at freezing point. Not being a chemist, I didn't understand all that happened. But that's no matter. For the lecturer went on to say that if you preferred to call it the melting point instead of the freezing point, that was all right; for the two were the same thing. It all depended, he said, on which direction you looked at it from. If you looked at it from the hot end of the thermometer, it was the freezing point; if you looked at it from the cold end, it was the melting point.

That struck me as very queer. Melting and freezing are just the opposite. You would think they would prefer the opposite ends of the thermometer; or at least get as far apart as they could. But that they should both pick out the same spot on which to do such opposite things as to melt and to freeze, and that what you call this spot depends merely upon which end of the thermometer you look at it from — that set me to thinking.

What I thought was that it is much the same

way with people. The freezing point and the melting point are close together with us all. If you come at us from one direction, this spot looks to you like the freezing point; and if you come at us from the other, it looks to you like the melting point.

Haven't you ever noticed that your mother, for instance — when you ask her permission to do something that you want to do very much, but that you are afraid from the start may not go through — is just at this melting-freezing point? If you come upon her from the right side and say just the right thing, or just the right thing happens at the right moment, then it is the melting point; but if you say the wrong thing, or just the wrong thing happens, why then it is the freezing point instead. I expect you have noticed that.

But you may not have noticed that there are people who seem to come at everybody on the freezing point side. No matter what it is — an election, a concert, a party, anything — they just freeze us up. And there are other people who somehow come at us all on the melting point side. No matter in what trouble and perplexities we are frozen fast, as soon as we meet these people we thaw out; we loosen up; the blood begins to run through us again; the sun is warm and the air is soft; and we feel as if we could live and labor and love as long as these

39

people are around. Have you ever noticed that? Well, you will notice it before you are as old as I am.

Finest of all the fine arts and greatest of all the great ones, finer than singing or painting, playing or speaking or any other art in the world, is this art of turning the freezing point into the melting point. Why don't we all begin to learn it right away?

THE WOMAN WHO
HELD ON TO THE BIG BOAT

When I was in Honolulu last summer, I went on an excursion to one of the other islands. We went in a big steamboat. At this other island they had no wharf long enough to take the big steamer. So you had to land in small boats.

I have done that many times, and it is always rather uncertain. You go down the outside of the big boat on some stairs which hang there by ropes and chains ("gangway," the sailors call it). The stairs are never very solid. You step from the platform at the bottom of these stairs into the smaller boat. That isn't very certain either. It generally moves away just when you are ready to step into it. When you do step into it, it is never quite where you thought it was going to be. There are some men who try to hold the small boat steady to the side of the platform. But so far as I have observed, they are never very successful.

On this trip I was speaking of, when it came time to land, there went down the stairs a woman who probably had the same feeling about the whole performance that I always had. If you are timid, and perhaps not very spry, it doesn't make you any spryer to have a whole steamerful of people looking at you.   So this lady went down the stairs.

On the platform, two sailors took hold of either arm to steady her.   The small boat stood still.   She stepped into it with both feet.   It was straight below the stairs, and close up. But she still kept hold of the rails of the platform on the big boat — with both hands, tight. Then the small boat moved away, without giving any notice whatever.   The lady's feet were in it, but her hands kept tight hold of the stairs. It looked as if something dreadful was going to happen.   Either the lady was going to be pulled apart, or else she was going to drop down into the ocean between the small boat and the big one.   Then the captain shouted to her, " Let go! "   She did, and the two men pushed her over into the small boat and she was all right.

The moral of this little incident is plain. Many people want to take hold of something new, but they don't want to let go of anything old in order to do it.   They want to be on the big boat and on the little one at the same time. It can't be done.   You have to stay where you are or make a clean jump of it.

THE SIGNING
OF THE CROSS

In one of the Southern states some years ago there was a governor who did great things for public education. Schools in the South were not very numerous or very good in those days. The rich people had always sent their children to private schools, or they had hired teachers to come into their homes and teach them. The idea of a great free public school system, where every child, no matter how poor his people were, could have the same opportunity as every other child, had not yet taken hold of the imagination of the South.

This governor was the man who, in his own state, did more than any and all other men to make the idea take hold. He traveled all around his state visiting the schools and seeing just how few and how poor they were. He went through the North and learned all he could about buildings, teachers, playgrounds and everything else. He talked with legislators, with business men, with lawyers, doctors and day laborers, to awaken in them a sense of what they were not doing and what they ought to do. And he built, finally, a school system in his state that made for every citizen an open door into the future such as they had never had before.

And do you know how he came to do it? Of course it needed to be done, and he saw that. But there were many other things that needed to be done also. What kept his eye on this one particular goal and never allowed it to wander once until he had reached it? I can tell you. It was a memory which he carried until his dying day and which no achievement of his own could ever rid him of.

When he was a small boy, his mother had sold a little piece of property. All the men that were party to the deal had signed their names, and the lawyer handed the deed to his mother to sign. But she hung her head and motioned for the lawyer to write her name for her. Then she made a cross beside it with her own hand. It was a hand he loved, and venerated as he grew older, a hand with strength and skill and kindness in it, but it couldn't write. And the boy made up his mind then that if God ever gave him a chance, he would save every woman in his great state the feeling of shame which both he and his good mother had had in that hour. And he did.

If ever there is anything wrong, anything humiliating like this, in your own history or in that of your own family, you can spend

44

your life merely being ashamed of it and trying to forget it and cover it up; or you can do as this man did — use it as a springboard from which to take a good, long jump ahead.

THE BOY
WITHOUT THE EYELIDS

One time I met a doctor from a little town in Virginia. Although it is a small town, there is a school in it for blind children, and this doctor was the physician for that school.

There was one boy in this school who didn't have any eyelids. You might think that if you didn't have any eyelids to be dropping down over your eyes you could see all the better. But it does not work that way. You can have too much light as well as too little.

The sun poured into this little fellow's eyes and the dust blew into them until at last he could see practically nothing, but went stumbling about with his hands up to his eyes, peering out like an owl. And all this time his eyes were about as bad to look at as they were to look through; so that the teachers hated to have him in their classes.

They brought this poor little fellow to the doctor. The doctor said he didn't know what he could do, but if the teachers would get the consent of the boy's parents, the doctor would do what he could.

Meanwhile he tried to find something in his books about boys who were born without eyelids, but there are so few such cases — only about one in ten million — that he couldn't find much. The case was perfectly simple: the boy had to be provided with some eyelids, that was all. Where to find them and how to put them on was the question.

The doctor thought it over and made up his mind. When the boy came back, he was ready to make him some eyelids. He gave him some ether, and when the little fellow went to sleep, he cut into the skin on his temples, and somehow — I don't quite know how — he slit the skin and the flesh across where the eyelids ought to have been, and sewed them fast.

Then he did the boy's head up in plasters for a week; and when he took the plasters off, the boy had some eyelids. They were just as good as anybody's eyelids, except that they did not have any lashes to them. But you don't need lashes anyhow — at least not unless you are a girl. What proved that the eyelids were all right was that the boy could wink as well as any other boy, and his eyes would open and shut like a doll's.

And now appeared a wonderful thing. As the boy began to use his new eyelids and to shut out the sun and the dust with them, he began to see just a little, and then a little more, until finally here was not only a boy with eyelids but a boy with eyes, and both the eyes and the eyelids as good as anybody's.

For this delicate and wonderful operation, the doctor received and expected nothing. No money, for the boy had none; no fame, for he has never published the story. He received nothing, except the gratitude of one small boy and the boy's mother.

It is a great thing to have skill, a steady hand, a cool head and a clear eye. And it is a great thing to have knowledge, and to know your business so well that if you ever have to, you can do something that nobody has ever done before you. But it is a much greater and finer thing to place your skill and your knowledge at the service of the humblest.

TURN
IT AROUND

I read in the paper the other day about an interesting social occasion.

General and Mrs. Young had been married twenty-eight years. When they began housekeeping, a girl named Maggie came to work for them. She has been with them ever since. Eleven years ago a second girl named Kate came to work for them.

A couple of weeks ago, General and Mrs. Young told Maggie and Kate that they might have a party in the Young's house at Beverly Hills. They were to invite whomever they wanted. They were to be hostesses and to manage the whole affair to suit themselves. All that General and Mrs. Young asked for themselves was the pleasure of waiting on the guests.

So Maggie and Kate had an afternoon tea. They invited sixty guests. Many of these were close friends of General and Mrs. Young's. That sounds fine too. I observed with special interest that among those present was Mrs. Young's mother who came all the way from Philadelphia for the party.

I presume there were others there whom General and Mrs. Young did not know, but were honored to meet. I hope the policeman

and his wife were there, and the night watch-
man at the mill, etc., etc. At any rate, Maggie
and Kate received, and poured, and owned the
house for the afternoon, and General and Mrs.
Young carried the trays and filled the coffee-
urns, and probably enjoyed themselves fully
as much as Maggie and Kate.

It would be a fine thing if we could all of
us change around like this once in a while. If
the man who sits in the pew had to preach once
a year, maybe he would listen a little better and
sit a little stiller and not look down his nose
quite so much, even when the preacher isn't
doing very well. And if the preacher had to
listen a part of the time, maybe he wouldn't
be so dead sure about what he preaches and say
so many things his people don't like.

If the schoolboy had to teach, one day in a
semester, and all the boys made as much trouble
for him as they could, maybe he would be a
little more patient with his own teacher. And
if the teacher had to study something she didn't
care anything about, while the circus parade
was going by and the calliope was playing a
couple of blocks off, and she knew that Bill
Jones, who is supposed to be at the dentist's,
was really following the parade, maybe the
teacher would not be so hard on the boys.

If the employer once in a while did the work
of the clerk, and the clerk worried about the

pay-roll; if the husband did the housework and the wife ran the store; and if we could all of us now and then change places with one another, maybe we would all of us be more patient with one another than we are.

Whenever you can, put yourself in the other's place. Turn the thing around and see how it works.

THE
RANCHER

◆　　◆

The other day I met a rancher. I have met ranchers before, but this was a new kind. And in a new place. It was away back in the mountains, just this side of Mt. Pacifico.

I had heard about this rancher and his wife — how they lived there all by themselves, ten miles from Colby's, fifteen from Opid's, twenty from Switzer's, twenty from Acton over in the Mojave desert, where they go to take the train; their nearest neighbor eight miles over the mountains — no postman, no telephone — and not a bag of cement, nor a wagon wheel, nor a sack of flour, nor anything else getting to them except on the back of a burro.

I had heard of them, I say. And I started for their place. The trail got fainter and fainter and longer and longer and finally dwindled down to a few cow-tracks. I had about concluded that they must have moved the ranch, when at last I stumbled upon it. Twenty-seven acres of land; one gold mine up on the side of the mountain, one garden, one saw mill, one house, one cabin for guests, one old barn and one new one, five cows, two horses, one burro, one flock of chickens, one rancher and his wife.

I wondered what sort of a man would go away to such a place to make a home for himself; and I found, for one thing, that he wasn't sour on anything or anybody. He had no grouch. He hadn't gone off by himself because he was mad. He wasn't there because it was the only kind of place he knew. He had lived in many states of the union and had been two years in Alaska, looking for gold. He knew the life of big cities, and he had once been captain of the Los Angeles Police Force. He wasn't there because he had been a failure in other places.

I asked him if I could send him some books, and he brought out a certain kind of religious book and said, " If you have any of this kind, send 'em to me. Stories I don't have time to read. I took the paper for six months after I came here, but it wasn't anything but murders and I stopped it."

The difficulties of his situation did not seem to make much impression on him. He admitted that once in a while one of his cows would fail to come home — probably bitten by a rattlesnake or eaten by a lion — and that once he had lost a drove of six burros. But that didn't impress him. What impressed him was that everything that he had there he had dug out of the ground or cut from the surface of it, by his own labor. " That cabin," he said, "was standing timber, three months ago."

And finally it came out, why he was there. "The average man in a city," he said, "just can't improve himself. He is crowded and hurried, he can't think for himself, so by and by he just gives it up and lives and thinks like everybody else. But up here in the mountains, where it is quiet and roomy, a man can think as much as he wants to, and he can't hardly help but get better."

I didn't want to live on his ranch. I was willing to give civilization at least one more trial. But I took off my hat to him, just the same. There are men who raise the standard of the human race. They make you think better of yourself and of everybody. Such a man is worth a day's journey, on foot, in the blazing sun, over the mountains, to see. Wherever you find one, see that you keep your mouth shut and your ears open. Maybe you can learn from him a secret that will keep you also pegging away on your own improvement as long as you live.

THE SAND-PILE
AND WHAT WASN'T IN IT

A sand-pile is a familiar thing. We had one in the neighborhood where I lived when I was a boy. It was not a little one that had been hauled in in a wagon, but a great, huge one that God Himself had made. I think I shall remember it as long as I remember any place in this world. But children who do not have a chance at a bigger one are lucky if their fathers and mothers have provided a little one for them in the back yard.

Some years ago, a woman in the town of Boxford, Massachusetts, at the beginning of the summer vacation had a load of clean white sand brought from the seashore to her back yard for her children to play in. The children played in it all summer. They built a whole town — paved streets and back alleys, an ice-house, a market, a coal-mine just outside the city limits, a garbage plant, a stone-quarry, houses and garages, stone walls, a shoe factory, a cotton mill, a department store. It was as nearly a complete city as you can build in a sand-pile.

But there were two things lacking; there was no church and no school-house. The mother of the boys felt a little bad about this when she

55

discovered at. But her boys didn't dislike to go to school, nor even to church; so she wondered about it and then asked them, " Why don't you have a school? " They answered, " Because it is vacation." Then she said, " Why don't you have a church? " And they replied, " Because we don't play in the sand-pile on Sundays."

But what I want to say to you is: while you are building, build for all the week through and all the year round. If you have nothing in your character but what you can use all the time and use right off, then the best part of you will be left out. When your mother wants you to learn something that you can't use this summer, or your father wants you to go to school a little longer, that's because they know that while you are building you have to build for a long time. You have to make your city complete.

THE
THANK-OFFERING

One time when I was raising a deficit in the church where I was preaching, a woman who was a stranger in the town and in the church made a subscription to it. I had never seen her before. She was not responsible for the church debt. Nor were any of her family. And yet she gave me some money for it. She told me it was a " thank-offering." " A thank-offering for what? " I asked. " A thank-offering," said she, " for the kindness of strangers in the world."

" In the world," she said. Not there in that town only — though I hoped she included us, or she wouldn't have made her thank-offering through us. But she made it for the kindness of strangers " in the world."

She had been a stranger on shipboard and a stranger in foreign countries; a stranger in hospitals and at health resorts. She had walked the streets of a town full of strangers, sick and alone and ten thousand miles from friends — and here she was again that Sunday, in a town of strangers, making a thank-offering for the kindness of strangers all around the world.

I wondered how it happened. For I have known so many people who have spoken in just the opposite way. Strangers are apt to be rough to a good many of us, and to try to get the better of us, and to take up all the room in the car that we ought to have, and to push in in front of us at the ticket office, and to interfere with our comfort in many ways. How did it come that they were always kind to this woman? Maybe the woman herself had something to do with that. If strangers are not kind to you, maybe it is because there is something wrong with yourself.

NO STRAIGHT
PATH FOR KINGS

It is related that the geometer Euclid once met King Ptolemy of Egypt. Euclid was the father, as we say, of the science of geometry. That is the science of lines and spaces, and of how many angles are in a triangle — you'll know about it, and be sorry for it, or glad, some time. Euclid knew more about all this than any other man of his time.

King Ptolemy was the greatest king of his time, rich, powerful and famous. The two men met. King Ptolemy asked Euclid about some problem, and Euclid started in to tell him. The king was impatient, and wanted Euclid to show him in some easier way. But Euclid said, " In geometry there is no straight path for kings."

Across the fields there might be such a path — even if the fields belonged to someone else — for the king could take them and do what he would with them. To the possession of some grand woman for his wife, or some palace for his sons, or some fine horse for himself to ride, the king might find a path; for the king had great power, and could take what he wanted. But when it came to knowledge, in and out among the circles and the triangles, or through the sky among the stars, there was no straight path for him just because he was a king. He'd have to find his way around like any ordinary man.

The best things of the world are open to us all on equal terms. You may ride in a better automobile than I do; but when it comes to making people like you, you can't ride any straighter toward that than I can. You may have more muscle and more good looks than I; but there's no straight path for you to knowledge or love or honor on that account.

In matters of little account, things may be uneven. But if it ever seems to you that somebody has a great advantage over you because he is rich or his father is well known or his mother president of the Federation, remember the man who stood up to Ptolemy and said, " In geometry there is no straight path for kings."

WHY DOESN'T
SHE GET A MEDAL?

Reading, now and then, of the people who get medals for being heroes, I often wish that a certain woman whom I know might have one.

She is a tall, fine-looking woman, getting pretty well along in years now, but as straight, and with as good command of herself, as when I used to worry her in the schoolroom thirty five years ago. Many women — perhaps most women — live useful and unselfish lives; but this woman has been a genius at it.

She always had a way of getting around people — and especially around boys. I never knew her to have trouble with a boy — and that was certainly not because the boys she had to deal with were angels — as I will tell you in a minute. When my father and mother used to be away from home for a few days, this lady would come and keep house for us. And when the folks got home, and she told them how good we had all been, they could hardly believe it.

We could hardly believe it ourselves. And yet it was true. For, somehow, you did what this lady wanted you to. Sometimes without knowing it, sometimes almost without intending it, but always without growling, you did what she wanted you to.

After she had taught a few years in the public schools, I suppose she wanted something harder; probably the boys weren't bad enough to suit her; so she got a position in a reform school. That was in the days when they weren't so good to boys in such a place as they are these days. She hadn't been there an hour before a boy who had just been whipped by the principal came into her room.

I presume he deserved the whipping, but this lady did not stop to inquire about that. All she noticed was that his wrists were black and blue. She called to him to show her what was the matter with him, and without asking him any questions about what he had done, she got a bandage and some soothing liniment and wrapped up his wrists.

This fellow proved to be a ring-leader among the boys. When he told the other fellows what had happened, and how the new lady had rubbed his wrists and done them up in witch-hazel, they were all for the new lady — and they continued for her — until through her influence the reform school became a place where you would almost be willing to go yourself.

This kind of work this lady did for thirty years. She had these " boys " of hers, as she always called them, scattered all up and down the country. Many of them used to come back to the reform school to see her; and if there were a good many of them who did not turn out well, they at least were sorry for her sake that they could not do better.

But the reason I think she ought to have a medal is that she has done all this work, for years, in almost constant pain. One of the nerves that runs up through her face and temple got diseased. Nothing could be done for it, so there was no use to stop. Besides, she loved her work, and she had her own living to earn.

But after a while, she heard that at the hospital of the Mayo Brothers, near whose town she lived, they sometimes removed this nerve. She went up to see if it could be done. The doctor told her that he did sometimes remove the nerve, but it was only when people were otherwise well and strong — and she was not. She asked him whether he would not try the operation, provided she stated in writing that it was at her own request, and that she would take the consequences. The doctor put his hand kindly on her shoulder, and said, " My dear madam, we don't commit murder here." So back she went, as she had come.

There is nothing very unusual about this story. I tell it to remind you that the heroes do not all get into the newspaper or on the Carnegie list. Many of them are plain men and women who work along from year to year;

they make no fuss, they attract no attention and they wear no medals. Look out for these heroes in plain clothes, and take off your hat to them when you see them. And it may be — it may be — that there is one of them in your own house.

THE
TOWN CLOCK

In the older and smaller towns of Europe, one of the most important institutions is the town clock. It strikes loudly and slowly, and people can hear it from anywhere in the village.

When the town was built, there were no such things as pocket watches, and few if any of the people had clocks in their own houses. Everybody went by the town clock. There was no dispute as to whose time was correct. In many of these towns, the people have kept down the cost of living to this day by continuing to depend on the town clock and by not investing in a watch for every member of the family.

Sometimes these town clocks were gaily ornamented with pictures or statues. Some of them had figures representing historical characters, and these figures at certain hours of the day came out of their niches above or at the side of the dial, and went through performances for the benefit of the audience.

In the town of Rothenburg, Germany, there is such a clock which is to this day not only the delight of the townspeople, but an attraction that draws hundreds of visitors from all parts of the world. When the clock strikes for noon, doors fly open at each side of the dials, and two figures come out. One represents an old burgomaster, the other a French general. The burgomaster drinks a scandalous amount of wine at one draught out of an enormous bowl, and the French general falls backward in astonishment. So the townspeople are reminded that once, by a similar feat, a burgomaster saved the town when it had been conquered by the French — and incidentally they know what time it is.

The other day I read for the first time of the part played by one of these town clocks in the history of its town. It was in Leyden in 1535. Some restless people had planned a revolution. They were to meet at a certain time and go to the houses of the magistrates. It is said that if they did not get what they wanted, they planned to burn the town.

The only clock they had to go by was the town clock. The magistrates heard of the plot, and discussed how to stop it. One of them proposed that they simply stop the clock an hour or two before the revolution was to begin. They did so. The people listened for the clock. It did not strike. They were thrown into confusion. They did not get together, and the revolution did not come off. The next day it was too late.

If this were a fable instead of a true story, I should say that the moral of it was that a public servant should serve the whole. A clock built by the town, depended upon by the town, should keep the town out of trouble. It will do this generally by keeping steadily on its way; but once in a while it may be necessary for it to do something extraordinary, as the town clock of Leyden did in 1535. But what it would want, if it could think, would be, not merely to be allowed to keep on forever without being disturbed, but to be used in any way so as to serve and save the people.

THE
SINGING WOMAN

Several years ago a lady wrote a poem entitled "The Singing Man." It is too long to quote. But the idea of it is that at first men were happy at their work and sang over it, no matter how hard it was. "He sang above the vineyards of the world," it begins. Then it goes on to say that men do not sing at their work any more, in the mines, in the factories — and the poem closes with the line, "Give back the singing man."

Now if the joy has faded out of any man's work, I am sorry. But I can see some reasons why men do not sing at their work these days, even though they may feel like it. I once worked in a sawmill. I used to feel like singing there sometimes, especially on Saturday afternoons when it was nearly time for the whistle to blow. But I never did, because it wouldn't have done any good. I couldn't have heard myself.

Undoubtedly there is not much singing in a boiler factory. Maybe some of the men working there feel like singing, but they can't compete. It wouldn't do to have everybody in a big office singing. The stenographer couldn't hear what was being dictated, and the manager would get the wrong note into his letters, and everything would be in a mess.

But there are still people in the world who not only feel like singing but who actually do it. One morning not long ago I was wakened by the sound of a phonograph in a little house on the back of the lot next door. It was playing the famous sextet from *Lucia*. But high and clear above the music of the phonograph was the pure soprano of a woman's voice, carrying the air.

You could feel the joy in that voice. It went like a brook, or like a bird — away up on the highest notes — you could hear it above Caruso and all the rest. Several times we heard it. Then there were two or three other selections — a regular morning concert — but always with the voice of the singing woman high and clear above everything else. An hour later when a member of my family was out in the back yard, the singing woman was out in hers, hanging up some clothes. She took the clothespins out of her mouth, threw up her head and said, " We are going to the beach. It is the baby's birthday."

So that was what she was singing about. Well, almost every holiday is somebody's birthday. And there is another thing that some folks haven't noticed: that there isn't any day on which somebody wasn't born. Every day is somebody's birthday. And it is the birthday of somebody that you like, or that you would like if you knew him. So why not sing any day? Being glad isn't all there is to being good. But I'll tell you this: nobody can be good who isn't also glad.

THE
CUCKOO

◆   ◆

The cuckoo is a bird with whom I have no personal acquaintance. But I have often heard him — or her — badly spoken of. The great criticism of her is that she will not build a nest for herself, but when she finds a good nest some other bird has built, she lays her eggs in that and goes off to have a good time.

She puts off upon someone else the trouble of hatching out her eggs and bringing up her children. That doesn't seem right. What makes it still worse is that the baby cuckoo is apt to be stronger than the other baby birds, and to have a bad disposition, and so to make the nest uncomfortable for the rest of the baby birds. But maybe his mother doesn't know that.

Mr. Charles Darwin, whose reputation with some folks is hardly better than the cuckoo's, once came to the cuckoo's defence. He said that the cuckoo didn't lay her eggs as most birds do — three or four within a few days — but several weeks apart. So, if she had a nest of her own, and laid one egg in it, and sat on that, a few weeks later she would be sitting on another egg and also on one or two of her children that had hatched out in the meantime.

That would be hard on the little cuckoos that had got far enough along not to enjoy being sat on. And when she had half a dozen little cuckoos in her nest, they would be of all different ages, and the bigger ones (you know how it is with children) would eat up all the food and make a bad household of it generally.

Besides that, the cuckoo is a migratory bird, as they call them. She is a kind of tourist. She stays a season in one place and then goes on to another. By the time she had her continued family raised, her other relatives would all be gone on to the next place and she would be left behind.

When I read these things that Mr. Darwin had said, I thought: the cuckoo is not a bad bird after all; she is only a wise one. She knows she can count on the motherly instinct of the robin, and that her little baby cuckoo will neither be starved nor put out of doors before he can fly. But to raise him herself, she can't. That's the reason she lays one egg in this robin's nest and another in that, and goes on. All very well, I am sure.

Quite wise, in fact; and I might stop with that. For if you think all the wisdom of this world is in folks like us, you are mistaken. Some of the little creatures of the earth know how to take care of themselves fully as well as we do.

But the thing I want you especially to learn from the cuckoo is that people may often get bad reputations which they do not deserve. Probably the birds understand each other, and I don't know that any robin ever complained of any cuckoo. But men have given her a bad reputation, because they did not understand. They knew what she did, but not why she did it.

When you hear it said of a boy that he is mean, or of a girl that she says bad things about other girls behind their backs, never take it just as it sounds. There may be some misunderstanding. There probably is. There usually is. In nine cases out of ten, people who have bad reputations don't entirely deserve them. You may get a bad one yourself sometime and not deserve it at all.

So remember, and when you hear anyone badly spoken of, stop and look up the facts before you believe what you hear. People said many bad things even about Jesus. But now that people know about him, all the world loves and praises him.

THE
WAITRESS

◆   ◆

A few weeks ago in New York I went into a
very unusual place to eat. It was a restaurant
called the Piazetta. It was a Spanish affair, or
maybe Italian. It was lighted with candles,
which give the worst light that can be had from
anything. At one side of a big room there was
a roof coming down into it, with red tiles on it,
so as to make you think you were out of doors
and looking up at the side of a house. In the
wall under this roof were windows, wide open,
and through these you could see people eating
at tables.

In another room you could see a fire burning
in a fireplace and a kettle boiling over it. The
waiters were colored girls. They wore black
dresses, bright blue aprons, and had orange
scarfs tied around their heads. There wasn't
so very much to eat except the atmosphere —
so far as I could see — but people seemed to
eat that up.

On the table at which I sat there was a little
silver standard with a card in it. I took the
card out and it read; " Miss Honoria Jackson
who waits upon this table is hereby given dis-
tinguished mention for her courtesy and faithfulness. This honor has been accorded to Miss

Honoria for three months in succession." When Miss Honoria saw me reading this, she smiled in a very friendly way and was more faithful and courteous than ever.

In some restaurants they do such things in the opposite way. They have a card that says, " Please report to the management any inattention or discourtesy on the part of the waiters." Not so good. Not nearly so good. There is an old saying that you can catch more flies with molasses than with vinegar. Very true. We all do like a little praise. There are simple words that are often worth more to us than money. When we have done our best, it is not enough that we should be paid for it. We want to know that there is somebody who has noticed it.

And I believe that there is Somebody who always does notice it. I believe that when we do badly, sometimes at least He looks the other way, for He knows that we are just awkward. But I believe that whenever we do well, then He is looking especially our way. Maybe somewhere on His table He has a card that makes special mention of us. Anyhow, He knows.

75

ANOTHER
WAITRESS

One time I gave some lectures at Berkeley and lived at the hotel. After three or four days, I became oppressed with the fact that I was living in more style than I was accustomed to, and thought it would be well for me, before I came home, to get down to my natural level. I went out and looked for a lunch counter. In every college town you will find them — the kind where the boys come in and sit down at a high counter, and talk it all over with each other and the waiters, and explain why the team didn't do any better. I found such a lunch counter, climbed up upon my stool, and felt that I was getting back to normal.

There was a nice young woman who waited upon me. I thought she was as good a waiter as I ever saw. When you wanted anything, she wasn't away off in the kitchen, as waiters generally are, or talking to the boys so that she couldn't hear you, but was right there looking at you and listening for you to say what you wanted. Or so it seemed to me.

Then I saw her looking at me as if she were trying to remember me, and after a while she came up and asked, " Aren't you the man who has been speaking evenings at the Congregational church? " I told her I was. " Yes," said she, " I met you there last night, with my husband. Professor Bade introduced us to you." Then I remembered her — only I hadn't expected to see her behind the lunch counter — and I asked about her husband. " He is studying," she said. " We are from the North. My husband had wanted to study for a long time — and Professor Bade and the other men here encouraged him to do it. So we just came — and we're getting along fine. . . . We enjoyed hearing and meeting you last night," said she, " but this is an unexpected honor I have in waiting upon you." " Give your husband good luck from me," I told her. " I certainly will," she replied. " And we will hear you tonight." And as I paid my bill, she said again, " It has been a great pleasure to me."

The next night I saw them; and I couldn't see but what they were about as good looking a couple as there were in the house. There were Professor Buckham and Professor Bade and the president of the School, and the dean of the Divinity School of Chicago University, and several other men of national reputation among scholars, and the waitress and her husband, all talking together as comfortably as you please. And I thought — well, I thought several things.

I thought first that it is a fine thing to do anything well. If it is only waiting on the table

77

at the lunch counter, it's a great thing to do that well, and to be an artist at it. Then I thought, what a fine thing for a young woman to be willing to help her husband that way! If he doesn't make good it isn't her fault. But mostly I thought, " the rich and poor meet together, the Lord is the father of them all."

We are brothers and sisters to all men and women. But if people love the same things as you do, if they love music as you do, or beauty as you do, or knowledge as you do, that is a cord that draws you to them right away. If you are after the right things, you'll meet the right people. And personally I came away from a great seat of learning, feeling specially under obligation to the waitress.

THE
MONUMENT

In San Francisco there is a monument that impresses me very much. It is on a corner of Market Street, where another street runs in at an angle and so makes a little open space. It has a granite base, and on this there are perhaps five figures, all in bronze. They are life-sized figures of men, working with some machinery — a huge steel punch, with wheels and shafts and pulleys lying around, as if it were the floor of a foundry or a machine shop.

The figures are fine, strong ones; the muscles of the men stand out. But these men are also thinking about what they are doing, they understand their work and are putting themselves into it. And on the base of the monument it says, " Dedicated to Mechanics, by James Mervin Donahue, in memory of his father, Peter Donahue."

Old dwellers in San Francisco undoubtedly know who James Mervin Donahue and his father Peter Donahue were, and what they have done in and for the city. I do not know. But that does not make the monument any the less interesting to me. For as I sat there on the stone bench and looked at it, and watched the men who came to rest there for a minute as I was doing, I could imagine it all: some honest, big-hearted, hardworking Irishman, coming to this country, beginning at the bottom, getting perhaps to be boss of his gang or of his department or of the whole big shop, but continuing to be a mechanic. Perhaps he brought up a big family of boys and girls, all husky and independent and forceful like himself. And then one of them — probably grown richer and moved up a way socially, but looking back with a great satisfaction not only upon his father but upon the fact that his father was a mechanic — may have put up this monument to him.

I thought of Carey, the great missionary. He was introduced, one time, to a gathering of rich and fashionable people in England as a man who had once been a shoemaker. He corrected his introducer by saying, " No; only a cobbler." And I thought of Livingstone who put up a monument for his father and mother, with the words " Poor and Honorable " on it. When someone said to him, " It ought to be " poor BUT honorable," he replied, " No sir. ' Poor *AND* honorable,' that's the way it goes."

We read news about famous men. We see their pictures. But the whole world rests on the shoulders of the unknown and ordinary people who go about their business every day and do it with their intelligence and their might.

AUNT JENNIE'S
HEART TROUBLE

In a little town named Brownville, Kentucky, lives an old lady whom they call Aunt Jennie Brown. Whether the town takes its name from her I do not know, but she is a well-known and much respected character in and around it. The town is high up in the mountains, where not many people come and go. One reason more do not come and go is that there are practically no roads to come and go on. When there is any road it is generally just a bed of a stream, half full of boulders. It is rough riding, when anyone tries to ride. Most people prefer to walk.

Aunt Jennie has walked for many years back and forth between the village and a school two or three miles away where she has sold her eggs and her coverlets. But about a year ago as she was walking this route, a man more venturesome than most of the natives drove up behind her in a wagon. Aunt Jennie had never been in a wagon. So when this man asked her to ride, the temptation was too much for her, and though she was somewhat afraid, she climbed in. She rode a short distance, and then asked to be allowed to walk again.

When she arrived at the school, she complained of not feeling well, and said she thought it was " heart trouble." They asked her if she had ever had heart trouble before, and she said, " No." Then she told about riding in the wagon, and quite forgetful of the fact that Brownville has an elevation of about four thousand feet, she said she thought it was the wagon that had given her the heart trouble because, she said, " It was so high."

When I heard this story I thought of how many people there are who ride too high in this world — so high they cannot see the boulders till they bump into them; so high they cannot see other people and consequently ride over their feelings or their rights; so high (some of them) they cannot see the laws and so ride right across them.

Believe me, sooner or later, as a result of this habit, they have worse heart troubles than Aunt Jennie. Sooner or later they strike the boulders and are thrown out, or the sheriff sees them and invites them to come down, and their friends are ashamed of them and their enemies hate them. Oh yes, they have their heart troubles, from riding so high.

THE
CONTEST

One day I was one of the judges at a speaking contest at a big high school.

There were six speakers, and they were all good. Three of them spoke on the Constitution, one of them on Webster and the Constitution, and two of them on Lincoln and the Constitution. They were all good, as I said. All fine, in fact.

But there was one boy who got hold of me as none of the others did. He was free with his audience, as if he were not afraid of them. He spoke as if he had just come around the corner and found us all there, and had taken the chance to tell us something. He "warmed up" to it like an old hand.

I didn't know how other people in the big assembly hall felt, but though I listened to all the speakers with pleasure, this one boy made me feel as if I were going to spill over. He shook me up. Hardened as I am by many years of both speaking and listening, my heart was stirred as I heard him.

I marked him for first place. When the decision was announced I found all the other judges had done the same. They had felt, while he was speaking, just as I had. We gave him first place because of the way he did his work. He earned it.

But there was another thing about this speaker. He was a colored boy. And while he spoke, it seemed to me that even if he had been the worst speaker on the program instead of the best, it would have been a wonderful thing merely that he spoke. For he spoke on Lincoln and the Constitution. And he was a colored boy.

In the dark days of the Civil War, this boy's grandparents were slaves. What would Abraham Lincoln have thought — while the prayers and cries of six millions of those poor black people sounded in his ears — what would he have said if anyone had told him, that sixty years later a black boy would be standing on the platform at Jefferson High, speaking to two thousand other boys and girls about Lincoln and the Constitution — and that he would win the prize? I think if he could have believed it, it would have cheered him more than cablegrams from all the kings and princes of the world. Maybe there is some sort of celestial radio by which he heard it that day.

Of all the books that have been written and the speeches that have been made on Lincoln and the Constitution, I wonder if any is more full of meaning than just the speech of an unknown colored boy at a big city high school.

Lincoln once defended the Constitution and the colored people; now the colored people defend the Constitution and the Man who so gloriously saved it.

So one generation pays back the debts of its fathers. So the love of one great human heart spreads over the continent and continues through the years. And so law and order and humanity get ahead.

A GIRL
I KNEW

Some years ago, a little country girl from South Dakota named Christine Iverson came to study medicine in the university in the town where I lived. She was a Danish girl, with blue eyes and red hair and a ruddy complexion. She was quiet in her manner, but very quick and decided. Everybody naturally took a liking to her.

She was going to study medicine and she did. In a class of a couple of hundred men students she stood at the head. Men do not usually like to have a girl stand at the head of the class, but they liked this girl. She worked for her room and board, stayed out occasionally half a year to teach, got a position in the medical school that paid her two hundred dollars a year, and finished at the head of her class.

At about that time I moved away from that town and lost track of her. She had come as a child from Denmark. She had lived on the plains of South Dakota. She had made her way through a great university. I supposed that, like many who had done similar things, she would go to Detroit or to some other big city, go into practice, and get for herself some of the luxuries of life which she had never

had and which she surely deserved. But I
had really forgotten where she went, if I ever
knew.

Then there came to me the bulletin of Yank-
ton College where she did her undergraduate
work. And in this bulletin there was the story
of Christine Iverson. She had gone as a medical missionary to Arabia. She had become very
skilful in operations upon the eye, and in that
hot country where the sun glares fiercely, she
used to perform, all alone, from two to three
hundred delicate operations in a year.

Then the war came on. She and her husband set up a hospital for wounded soldiers.
They took care especially of the Turks,
who had been their worst enemies. I can just
see those Turks and Mussulmen and Ar-
menians and Englishmen " standing around "
when she told them to — for she was that
kind.

For three years she worked as doctor and
nurse, and her hospital at Busrah became a
famous place. Then came the typhus; and
like many another hero of war and peace this
little Danish girl lies buried somewhere near
the head of the Persian Gulf. " The Country
Gentleman " had an article about her, entitled
" Just a Country Girl," and her life has now
been written in a book.

It is a long way from Denmark to Arabia,

especially when you go by way of South Dakota; but this girl had spirit enough to make it. You think better of the possibilities of all boys and girls when you know a girl like this one.

PERFUME
IN THE HACK

◆   ◆

Some years ago when Madame Sarah Bernhardt was at the height of her fame, she was playing in Louisville, Kentucky. On her opening night the city was so crowded, and all the carriages had been engaged so far ahead, that she had great difficulty in getting one to take her to the theater. Someone found for her, at last, an old tumble-down hack, drawn by a raw-boned horse, driven by an old colored man who was almost as near falling to pieces as the rest of his outfit. It was the only coach in town so bad that nobody had engaged it.

The coach somehow appealed to the great singer. She probably had never seen one like it — or perhaps she was taken with the old man and wanted to be nice to him. Anyway, she told him to come back for her when the performance was over. He did so. A policeman saw him, among the uniformed coachmen. He looked at the old horse, hanging his head among the Kentucky thoroughbreds, and ordered the old man away. The old man said no; he had brought Madame Bernhardt to the play and he had come after her. That only made the officer laugh, and the old darkey had to move on.

He slipped into the line a little farther down, where another officer found him and ordered him out again. The old colored man knew what he was about, and he did not propose to lose either the money or the honor that was coming to him. So he climbed slowly down from his box, and opening the door of his old coach, said to the officer, " If you don't believe I brought Miss Sarah down here, you just smell the inside of my hack."

There is an influence left by the presence of great persons which is like the fragrance of Madame Bernhardt's perfumed garments. It is not made in any artificial way, but just produced by what the person is. A fine lady calls on your mother, and the parlor seems different for the rest of the afternoon. A great man comes through the town; you look at him, and there is more ozone in the air. It is said you can never see an angel, but you can sometimes hear the rustle of her wings as she goes by. A blind man was sitting by the road-side once, and he asked, " Who is going by? " and they told him, " Jesus."

Goodness is unmistakable, like the perfume of a rose. Watch for the people who leave an aroma of it behind them. Maybe you will catch some of it yourself.

YOU TURN
OUT; WE CAN'T

I saw this sign on the front end of a street car: " Autos turn out. We can't." I studied it, and I call it a good sign.

Strange that the street car companies should have to hang it out! The automobile can go anywhere. You may be where you have a perfect right to be, and yet you may be run into by an auto. But the street car will never go anywhere it doesn't belong; and if you get run into by a street car it will be because you are in its own right of way.

I didn't need this sign myself. For I made up my mind long ago that if anyone ever picked me up dead from under a street car, I wouldn't say a word, because I would know it was my own fault. But since there are so many people who do not feel this way, but think they have as much right on the track as the cars have, I hope all passing automobile drivers read this sign and thought about it — " Turn out; we can't."

There are many things for which we have to " turn out." A boy doesn't get his lessons, and at the end of the year he wishes the rules could be suspended so he could go on with the rest of the boys. But there has been a sign, all the year, in every teacher's eye, and all over the building, and if he had been half awake he could have read it: "You turn out; we can't."

I had a letter last week from an old friend of mine back East who wanted me to go and see two boys who are in jail here. They had stolen an automobile back in Illinois and had driven it through to California; and I guess they stole a good many things on the way, and did some other things just as bad. Of one of them my friend wrote, "He always thought he was smart enough to get away with it." But the only place for him to get away to now is the penitentiary, so far as I see.

For there has been a door standing wide open for both of these fellows. If they had looked down to the end of the road when they got into their stolen auto, they would have seen it.

It is the door of the Los Angeles jail. And over that door there was a sign that these boys ought to have been able to read clear back in Illinois where they started from. The sign runs: "You turn out; we can't."

There are right and wrong; there are laws made by God and made by man; there are the judgments of people on what we do; there are a thousand things in this world that have this same sign up in big letters: "You turn out; we can't." If we expect the whole round world and all the things and people in it to get out of our way, we are in for a smash-up. "You turn out; we can't."

THE
WORSHIPER

Several years ago, two men were walking up Barclay Street in New York from the ferry that had brought them over from New Jersey. It was Sunday morning, and as there were very few people on the street, their attention was drawn especially to an Italian woman a little way ahead of them. She had the appearance of being an immigrant who had just arrived. She wore a bright red shawl, a handkerchief over her head, and was otherwise dressed in her Sunday best. As she was passing one of the stores she stopped suddenly, dropped to her knees on the pavement, put up her hands and began to pray. The two men were surprised that she should take the sidewalk for such a purpose.

When they came up to her, they saw that the store in front of which she had knelt had a window full of crosses, Bibles and images. She had come from a country where almost at every corner you might see a road-side figure of Jesus with his cross, before which people stopped and said their prayers, and left their flowers in token of their gratitude. It was her first day in America, and when she passed this shop she did not stop to see that it was only a store. The sight of the familiar and beloved objects woke in her heart the impulse of gratitude and she knelt worshiping there in the street.

There is something like that in us all. Some people lose it as they go along, and some people keep it. But it is a thousand times better to keep it, even if you see something holy where it wasn't intended, than it is to have your eyes shut in a world so full of things that speak of the power and love of God. It is a barren world for people who can find nothing to worship.

THE
SHEPHERD UP-TO-DATE

◆　　◆

The shepherd has always been the great example of human faithfulness. Jesus spoke often of him, his care of his flocks, his personal interest in every one of them. He likened God to a shepherd, who would look for His sheep till He found them: He spoke of himself as " The Good Shepherd," and that is one of the world's favorite names for Him.

I have a picture of a shepherd taken in the North of England near Ambleside. The hills rise in the background behind him. He has walked over them during the night, and it is growing light. His dog walks beside him. On his shoulders he is carrying a sheep — holding the front feet in his right hand and the hind feet in his left. And underneath the picture it says, " He layeth it on his shoulder."

Two weeks ago I was driving through the desert, a few miles off the main highway this side of Bakersfield. Down the road came a burro, with a bell tied around his neck and a pack on his back. Then a flock of sheep — fifteen hundred of them — with two or three men on horseback and several on foot, and the proverbial dogs bringing up the rear.

And yet it wasn't quite the rear, either. For

when we got a quarter of a mile beyond them, there was an automobile, a good, big, easy-riding automobile, with a man at the wheel driving slowly and stopping now and then to let the flock get out of his way. In the back of the car, there was an abundance of coats and blankets; and there, looking out upon the landscape from as nice and soft a bed as anyone could wish, was a sheep. I didn't find out what was the matter with him — a broken leg, perhaps — or something worse, but whatever it was, there he lay, and rode, comfortable as you please.

Times change. Old ways give place to new ones. But faithfulness, gentleness, kindness, are immortal.

THE
FIREMAN'S SPEECH

The other day I got caught in a place where I had gone to eat my lunch. Before I could get out somebody got up and said they were going to have a speech. I didn't really have time to listen to a speech; but I had paid for my dinner and I didn't propose to leave it. Then the chairman introduced the Chief of the Fire Department. Before he began, I made up my mind I would stay till I had finished my dessert. But before I knew it I had stayed clear through. I forgot to leave.

The fireman began by saying he didn't know how to make a speech. Then he told us many things we didn't know. He said most of us didn't know where the nearest fire-alarm box was — and I began to wonder where mine was, and couldn't remember. He said that if we had a fire, we wouldn't know what number to call on the phone until we had stopped to look it up — and I said to myself, " That's so."

He said that on the average one garage caught fire every day and that some men would always light a match to see how much gasoline they had in the tank. He said that whenever there was a fire, everybody who was out in his auto started for it, and filled up the streets for blocks around so that he couldn't get near it. And I said to myself, " I'll never do that."

He was not strong on grammar, and said a few things that would not have got by your teacher. But when he said again, " I ain't no speaker. I been in the fire department ever since I was a kid. I don't know anything except how to fight fire," I said to myself, " If you only knew it, you are making one of the best speeches I ever heard. How many speeches I have listened to that were proper and polished and scholarly that couldn't hold a candle to yours! "

The moral of this is plain. The man who does things is always interesting. It is always easy to talk when you have something to talk about. When you have to write a composition in school, the reason you have such a time over it is that you really haven't anything you want to say. Get something on your mind that you want to get off, and it will come off in good shape. Do something, and people will always be glad to hear you tell about it. Deeds first, talk afterwards.

ASK THE
RIGHT MAN

I was standing one day recently on the third or fourth floor of one of our big department stores. A lady got out of the elevator, walked toward me, and said, " Kitchen stools." I didn't quite understand, and I said, " Beg pardon? " So she said again, this time with a rising accent, " Kitchen stools? " Then I understood. She wanted to know something about these articles. But she had asked the wrong man.

We are always doing that. We entertained a big convention in a church recently. We had had a great deal of experience with people asking other people where this or that place was, only to be told, " I don't live here." So we got a badge, reading, " Ask ME; I live here." We pinned these badges on certain people and had them circulate through the crowd, so that strangers would know whom to ask and would therefore ask the right man.

Life is full of questions for us all. It is a great thing if we can learn to put them to the right persons. If the water-pipe has gone wrong, and the doctor comes in, we don't ask him how to fix the pipe. We send for the plumber. If the plumber is at the house, and some member of the family has a sore throat, we don't ask him how to cure it; we send for the doctor. We don't ask the garage man about the geraniums nor the Japanese gardener about the spark-plugs.

I lay it down as a principle for you: Ask the right man. If you have lost your way down town, ask the policeman. He knows. If you are a girl, traveling away from home, don't ask the waitress at the depot restaurant, ask the Y.W.C.A. matron; that's what she is there for. If you want to know some secret of life that has not yet been revealed to you, don't ask the boy or girl across the aisle from you in school; ask your father or mother — that is what they are for.

A GOOD
MEMORY, CERTAINLY!

In a book about the Civil War, the writer tells some good stories about General Sherman. Two of these have to do with his remarkable memory. Early in the siege of Vicksburg, General Grant wanted some boats put over the bar from the Mississippi into the Yazoo River. The water was high; but just how high it was and whether high enough to allow the boats to run over the bar, nobody seemed to know. Several river pilots were asked, but none of them knew. General Sherman, then only a lieutenant, was there. After a little he said that he could tell them how high the water was. He told them. They took his statement, put the boats across, and found he was right.

When they asked him how he knew about the height of the water, he said, " Thirteen years ago I was coming up the Mississippi on a cotton boat that went into the mouth of the Yazoo River. The water was about as high then as it is now. I stood on the bow of the boat, and I remember the depth of the water that the man called who was heaving the lead." A good memory, certainly!

There was another instance quite as striking. While General Sherman was on his march to the sea, he was standing one day on the edge of an abandoned cotton field. An old white mule was trying to find something to eat in the field, and General Sherman seemed much interested in him. After a while he asked some soldiers to drive him up to the fence where the mule stood. Then he told one of them to clip the hair off the mule's right shoulder and see if he did not find a U. S. brand there. Sure enough, there it was. They asked General Sherman how he knew it was there. He replied, "When I was Depot Quarter-Master at New Orleans at the close of the Mexican War, I sold a lot of mules to some Southern planters, and this was one of them." When the history of the mule was learned from the owners of a plantation near by, it was found that the General was correct. A good memory.

But there is a kind of memory I wish we all had. I wish we had a memory that would keep all the good things and drop out all the bad. There are people who have the opposite kind. They remember all the slights they have had. Every disagreeable thing that has happened to them, every unkind word that anybody has said, sticks to them like glue. But all the sweet and lovely things run through their memory as if it were a sieve. You'd better forget everything you ever knew than to have a memory of that kind.

There was a poet once who had the good kind of memory. When he grew old he wrote a verse about a little girl who had been nice to him many years before. It ran this way:

" Jennie kissed me when we met,
 Jumping from the chair she sat in.
 Time, you thief, who like to get
 Sweets into your book, put that in.
 Say I'm weary, say I'm sad,
 Say that health and wealth have missed me.
 Say I'm growing old, but add —
     Jennie kissed me."

Nobody can remember everything — not even General Sherman. If we could, our minds would get so full of stuff that we couldn't use them. They would be like a shop so full of goods that people couldn't get in to buy anything. And much of it would be mean old stuff that would only be a nuisance to us. Nobody can remember everything. Many things must go. Get into the habit right now of keeping the good things and throwing out the bad ones. When anybody says a mean thing to you, forget it. But when anybody does you a kindness, nail it down to the floor of your memory so that it will never get away.

THE MAN
ON THE FENCE

We often speak of people who are " on the fence," meaning people who do not know what they think and cannot or will not get down on one side or the other. They are neither for nor against, neither one thing nor another — just " on the fence."

We do not like these people who are always on the fence. We like them to be one thing or another, so that we can count on them and know where we will find them. And I think it must be just as uncomfortable for these people themselves as it is for the rest of us. Almost anything is bearable when you get into it, but it wears your life out to be always on the fence.

During the war, I read about a man who was on the fence in a very different way. The story is told in a little book of letters written to his father by an American boy in France. And this is the story:

During a fight between the British and the Germans, a British officer saw a German officer hanging on the barbed wire fence that separated the trenches. He could not get down on the German side and run to his own trench. He could not get down on the British side and surrender. He could not move. He just hung there, where the shells flew the thickest. Over him and under him and all around him they went, and everybody who saw him expected that he would be blown to splinters at any moment.

The British officer watched him for a while and then said, " I can't bear to look at that poor chap any longer." So he went out between the trenches. It was a wonder he himself did not get caught by a shell. But he did not and neither did the man on the fence. The British officer went straight toward him, and before anyone knew what he was doing, he had taken him off the fence, discovered that he was exhausted, put him upon his shoulder, and was carrying him toward the German trench. The soldiers in both trenches saw what he was doing, and stopped firing; and when the British officer laid the German officer down, the German commander came out of the trench, took off the iron cross from his own coat, and pinned it on the coat of the British officer.

An American boy saw it with his own eyes. When you hear so many stories of how cruel men are in war, remember also this story of the man on the fence.

KIPLING
AND DANNY DEEVER

There is a poem of Rudyard Kipling's called "Danny Deever." It begins,

"What are the bugles blowin' for,
Said Files-on-parade,"

and goes on to tell what happened to Danny Deever. This poem was set to music by a great American musician, Walter Damrosch, and was made famous in this setting by a great American singer, David Bispham. Mr. Bispham tells the following story about himself, the song, and the author of the poem:

"When Kipling visited New York in 1889, I met him at an evening reception given in his honor. Though it was not a musical party, toward the close of the evening I was requested to sing "Danny Deever." At the conclusion of the song, Kipling arose, hastily said good-by to his hostess, and left the room. Everyone present was surprised, for they had wished to congratulate him on the power of his poem. After recovering from the attack of pneumonia brought on that very night by leaving the hot drawing-room for the snow-storm outside, he returned to England.

" The next spring I had a visit from a gentleman who called ceremoniously and politely informed me that his friend Kipling, who was in the country, sent me his apologies and regrets for what I might have thought his rudeness in leaving the room so suddenly after my singing of his ' Danny Deever ' in New York the winter before; but Mr. Kipling would like me to know that he had been so powerfully affected by my rendering of the ballad that he could not trust himself to speak and had to say good-night as quickly as possible."

When I read this little story I thought of two or three things. I thought, for one thing, that we must be careful about judging other people. What looks like rudeness may be something quite different, as in this case. I thought also that no man is too big or famous to apologize or explain, when he thinks he may have hurt the feelings of another. If you ever feel too big to do it, you are mistaken. You aren't big enough.

But mostly I thought of something Mr. Frederick Warde said the other evening. He remarked that, among a company of great artists with whom he worked for many years, there were never any jealousies. Every one of them was glad when another one got generous applause, even though he did not get much himself. " That did not mean," he said, " that we didn't wish we could do it well enough ourselves to get the same applause; but we were always glad for whoever did get it."

Jealousy is a big word, but the thing it stands for is the trait of small people. If you can't admire other people, you may be sure of one thing; nobody will ever waste much time admiring you.

THE MAN WHO
MOVED THE LANDMARK

The other day I was walking along Eighth Street between Broadway and Spring. There was a sign standing on the sidewalk, " Do not park between this sign and the alley." A man was just driving up in a machine, and I wondered whether he saw the sign; for I thought sure he could not get his machine in in front of it. The sign was a little one, and instead of being nailed to a post it was set on a standard.

So the man drove up, and got out of his machine. The machine stuck out about two feet beyond the sign. The man looked up and down the street, and then he just picked up the sign and set it down two feet nearer to the alley than it had been. There he read it — as I did — and it said, " Do not park between this sign and the alley." And he hadn't.

But I thought at once of the old text: " Remove not the landmark which thy fathers have set." I believe it is good advice. For if any man can drive up to any sign and move it to any place he wants to, nobody can say what might happen. He might come to a sign that says " Dump rubbish here," and he might take that sign and put it in your front yard. Or he might take the sign from the Dancing Academy and put it on the Jewish Temple or the Congregational Church, and much confusion might result.

And I remember thinking that it would be good enough for this man who moved the sign on Eighth Street, if someone should drive out of that alley and bump him good and hard. But I couldn't wait to see whether anyone did.

Landmarks are made to be left where they are put. As you go through life you see many of them. Some of them will be in your way, and it would be much more convenient for you if they were a little to this side or to that. Let them alone. For there is such a thing in the world as order. And because we have a reasonable amount of it, we can get in and out among people and things without getting killed. But if each of us is to make the whole world over to suit himself, nobody can safely go anywhere.

Customs that you don't just see the use of, habits that your fathers and mothers teach you, things that have been marked as sacred and beautiful by hundreds of generations that have gone before — they are landmarks that teach you how to steer and where to park.

THE
LABEL

A label is a very important thing. If you should get the wrong label on the medicine bottles, and give the baby for his whooping-cough what grandpa ought to have had for his rheumatism, the results might be serious. Manufacturers are very particular about their labels and often bring lawsuits against others for using them. Sometimes we are not quite sure whether we like certain things or not until we see the label on them.

Now people get labeled, just as things do. It is very important whether you get the right label on you, or the wrong one. If you are an honest man, but someone has pinned a tag on you saying that you are dishonest, and you go through life wearing this wrong tag, that is dreadful. If you are dishonest, and someone has pinned an " honest " tag on you, that is just as bad.

And if you pin the wrong tag on yourself, or get someone else to do it, sooner or later someone will come along who will take this wrong tag off you and put the right one on. For nothing is more important than that each one of us should wear the right label.

I heard an amusing instance the other day

of a man wearing first the wrong tag and then the right one.   At a certain university where they have military drill, they organized a hospital corps.   A lot of the boys had been drilling on a field some distance from the campus, and one of them had got very tired of it.   He saw the hospital corps coming; and he got one of his comrades to pin a tag on him, reading, " Wounded in leg; carry."   Then he lay down by the side of the road like a wounded soldier.

The hospital squad came along.   They were rather new at their work, and seeing this soldier lying there with this tag on him, they put him upon a litter and four of them carried him toward home.   But the man who was tagged enjoyed his ride so much, that the men who carried him began to suspect that he had labeled himself.   So after some consultation, they laid him down by the side of the road and pinned a tag on him that read, " Shot in head; walk home."   And so he walked.

It happens so to most of us sooner or later. Tag ourselves — or get our friends to tag us — however we will, we never come to the end of the journey without getting the right label.

THE DIME
FROM JESUS CHRIST

Everybody likes a man who cannot be beaten. I knew such a man some years ago, and with him goes the story of " The Dime from Jesus Christ."

He was a little Englishman who used to run a midnight mission in Chicago. After his meeting one evening, a man came to him and told a pitiful story. It was in the old days when the saloons were wide open, and Mr. Cooper (for that was his name — Alexander Cooper) was always on his guard against being fooled. That wasn't because he was stingy, but because, as he told me, if the men who came to his mission got the idea that he could be " worked," he couldn't do anything with them at all. They wouldn't respect him if they knew they could get ahead of him. So when a man asked him for money, he gave him food if he was hungry; or a coat if the needed it; but never money, unless he was sure of him.

But this man told him a pitiful story. It was late at night. The weather was stormy and cold. The man looked honest; he certainly was needy; and Mr. Cooper gave him a dime.

" As soon as I let go of that dime," he said, in telling me the story, " I knew I was beat."

So when the man shuffled out of the hall in search of food, the little man followed him. Down the street he went, splashing through the slush, and down a flight of steps into a dirty half-lighted den, with the little man behind him.

Up to the bar swaggered the man with the dime, and called out in a voice to attract the attention of all the men in the place, " Give me the bottle." Then, throwing the money down with a slap of his hand, " I got that from Jesus Christ," he said. Quick as a thought, the little man had his hand upon it. " If you did," said he, " 'e's got it back again." And out of the door he bolted, before anyone knew what had happened.

Probably none of you will ever be running a midnight mission. And probably you will never be dealing with men whom you will have to look out for as sharply as this man did for his (though I am not so sure of that). But anyhow, you will, without doubt, find yourself in many a hole of one sort or another. And when you do, you can say to yourself, " Oh, well, I am in this one. I'll watch out for the next one, but no use to try to get out of this." Or you can do as this little Englishman did — get out of *that* one.

THE
UNICORN

When I was a boy, I was anxious to know
about the unicorn. Just curiosity I suppose —
and because we didn't have any unicorn in my
neighborhood. My principal source of information about him was the Bible. From this
source I learned that he was a very strong animal; for Balaam, in the book of Numbers, says
that God Himself has, as it were, the strength
of a unicorn. I knew he had one horn, standing
up between his eyes, because that is where he
got his name, and it is what the Bible generally
mentions about him. Besides, I had seen the
picture of him.

Outside of the Bible I had one source of information about the unicorn. From this source
I knew that

" The lion and the unicorn were fighting for
the crown;
The lion beat the unicorn all about the town.
Some gave them white bread, some gave them
brown,
Some gave them plum cake and sent them out
of town."

Just when and where the lion and unicorn
fought for the crown I did not know. Then I

learned that on the English royal coat of arms since the union with Scotland, there has been a unicorn on one side and a lion on the other. The Scotch objected to the lion being on the right side and the unicorn on the left and also to taking the crown off the unicorn's head as the English wanted. Perhaps this is how the lion and the unicorn came to be fighting for the crown. For a long time this was all I could learn about the unicorn.

Then once I saw the statement of an old writer that the unicorn never allows himself to be taken alive. That agreed with my experience, for I never had seen a live one. Then I read this statement quoted from an old French book written in the thirteenth century —

" Of all animals there is none so dangerous as the unicorn; it attacks everybody with the horn which grows on the top of its head. But it takes such delight in young ladies that the hunters place a maiden on its trail. As soon as the unicorn sees the maiden, it lays its head in her lap and falls asleep, when it may easily be caught."

After I had acquired all this information about the unicorn, I learned one thing more. I learned that there isn't any such animal and never has been, and that all I had read about his great strength and his terrible fierceness was just imagination. And then I wondered how people could know so much about an animal that didn't exist.

Then I began to suspect that I had wasted my time on the unicorn. Wouldn't it be better to know a little about things that are, than so much about things that aren't? What was the use of all the knowledge I had acquired about the unicorn, if there wasn't any unicorn?

THE AUTOMOBILE
AND THE DIAMOND

When I went out to Los Angeles for the first time, I saw an automobile that was out of the ordinary. I do not know of what make it was originally. I guess it was not of any make. It looked as if some man (or boy) had picked up some wheels in one place, some axles in another, and had built his own automobile.

I ought to have written down a description of it at the time. The thing I remember most distinctly about it was the exhaust pipe. It had a tin can wired over the end of it, and this tin can was painted red and punched full of little holes. All I can say by way of describing the rest of it is that it all looked as if it belonged with the exhaust pipe. It was painted in a variety of colors, part red, part black, with green trimmings. I don't believe you would see just such another automobile in all the world.

But what attracted my attention most about this automobile was the sign on it. It read, "For sale; $190 cash; or will trade for a diamond." Trade for a diamond! I did not see the man who owned the machine, but I thought, "What would any man who would make and ride in such a machine do with a diamond?" Would he wear it? If he did, and if he looked anything like his machine, he would certainly cut a figure with a diamond! And if he wore the diamond, what would he ride in? He certainly would not have in his garage another automobile like the one he wanted to trade.

So I wondered about it; but I did not meet the owner and so I could not ask him. What I did think was that we all need many different things in this world. No two things could be less alike than a diamond and this automobile; and yet here was a man who didn't care which of them he had. He could use either of them equally well! And especially I thought how we need not merely practical things, things to ride in etc., but things to make us look well, things we don't really need — things that are merely to look at.

I never had a diamond, never expect to have one, and wouldn't know what to do with one if I had it. But still, what would the world be without diamonds? I know that. I remember that Mohammed once said, "If a man has two loaves of bread, let him sell one and buy a hyacinth." For we live not by practical things alone, but by pretty and attractive things as well.

THE MAN
WITH THE BROOM

One morning during the war I was coming down the street earlier than usual, when few people were about. One other man and I appeared to have the street all to ourselves. The other man was coming toward me, walking in the gutter and pushing a broom along in front of him. He had on the white coat of a street-sweeper, and was a fine, clean, intelligent-looking man. I saw he was a foreigner of some kind. I thought he might appreciate having someone say good-morning to him especially on such a fine morning, even if he could not understand anything more.

As we met, he stopped; and before I could say "good-morning," he had said, "What she spik in de pippa?" I did not quite understand at first, so he said it over again, "What she spik in de pippa?" Then, seeing that I still hesitated, he added, "about Italy?"

Then I understood. He was an Italian. He hadn't seen the paper; perhaps he could not read it; and he had hailed me as the first man he had seen that morning who could give him news of his native land. When he had asked me, "What she spik in de pippa?" it had not occurred to him that I might not know that he meant about Italy.

I replied, " I haven't seen this morning's paper." Then he said, " What she spik last night? " I was glad it was that morning he asked me, and not earlier in the week. For the news had been bad from Italy. The Italian army, after winning the praise of all the world for its bravery for many months, had suddenly weakened, turned, given way. Venice was in danger. There was talk of moving the capital. It had looked bad for Italy. But the very day before, the Italian army had halted, turned, broken through the Austrian line with a bayonet charge.

I was glad I had this kind of news for my friend with the broom. I gave it to him. His eye brightened. " She goin' hold 'im? " he asked. I said I thought she was, without doubt. " Pretty good for Italy," he said. And pushing his broom before him he went on up the street. I looked back at him, and imagined that he walked almost like a soldier. Maybe he imagined that his broom was a bayonet, and that he was pushing it through the Austrian line.

I got the morning paper, and I read not merely that the Italian army continued to " hold 'im," but I read of the great Italian colony in Southern California, and of how many men it had sent back to fight in the Italian army. The man with the broom may have a son among them.

Anyway, whoever you are and whatever you grow up to be, whether you push a broom, or a pencil, or a big business, and no matter where you push it, let your first thought of the morning be for your native land. Hope for her, pray for her, and may "what she spik in the pippa" bring you news of her welfare.

THE
CONCERT

◆ ◆

I went one evening to hear a concert given by an orchestra of grade school children. It was a wonderful thing. If there was an orchestra of any kind in the town where I was brought up, I don't remember it. People had a piano and a drum and a fiddle or two to dance by; but as for a real orchestra, I don't think I ever heard one till I was grown up. And when I saw two hundred and thirty-three boys and girls, picked out of twenty-five hundred that had been in training, standing there serious, earnest — nobody trying to show off or to draw attention to himself, nobody trying to be funny, but each one tending to his own business as if he were the whole thing and it all depended on him — it sounded to me like the prophecy of a better world coming.

For life is, when you think of it, a kind of orchestra, a kind of an attempt to make some sort of music, all through. Only some of us never get tuned up, and so we play a little off the key all our lives. Some of us who aren't appointed to lead, but only to beat the drum or play the traps, think we could lead better than the director, and that makes trouble. And every now and then one of us who is playing the cymbals thinks he ought to play the violin or the trombone, and he makes a fuss about that.

Some of us think the music ought to be louder there or softer here, and we are unhappy over that. Some of us think the leader goes too slowly, and some others of us can't keep up with him as it is. And every now and then someone won't play at all because he can't play the instrument he wants to or have it all his own way. And so the music of our life often gets badly twisted and tangled.

If we can learn to watch the leader, to stand up straight, and play our own parts without grumbling; if we will not waste time looking around to see whether the other fellow is doing what he ought to, but just put in the notes that are written down for us, and if we will keep that up all our lives, we will have a good deal better harmony.

FIFTY POUNDS
OF ICE, PLEASE!

A certain colored boy who recently moved with his parents to a Northern city, was found to be much behind in his school work. He was fifteen years old, but they had to put him in the second grade. The teachers naturally thought he must be very dull. Then they learned that in the town where he had lived down South, his teacher had been the village iceman. " He didn't come to school," said the boy, " till after he was through totin' ice around. Then if anybody wanted ice they comed after him. He wasn't learnin' me anything, so I quit."

How would you like to be in the middle of a recitation in geography, just telling your teacher what kind of grain grows on the banks of the Orinoco River, when someone would put his head in the door and call out to the teacher, " Fifty pounds of ice, please! " and he would put on his hat and go? I asked how you would like it. That's not a good way to put it. I shouldn't wonder if some of you would like it only too well. But how much would you learn? Little or nothing, to be sure.

What we all need in this world is a chance. We can't ask for anybody to push us, or to pick the stones out of the road for us, or to hold the door open while we go through, but we can ask for just a fair chance. Some folks don't have it. The boy who had the iceman for his teacher will be behind, all his life, on that account. When you see a boy who is as smart as you are but has twice as much work to do outside of school, or who could be captain of the ball team instead of you if he didn't have so many papers to carry, do what you can to give him a chance. It's what we all want in this world.

THE
ACCIDENT

These are days of accidents. You can hardly go down town without seeing a machine on the curb with part of its gear wrapped around a telephone pole or a hydrant. Every day on some street corner you see the broken glass that tells you that there was a smash-up there a little while before.

Four weeks ago today, I was walking down the street of a city in Michigan when I heard a crash and at the next corner saw an automobile turn over and light upon its top, its wheels still spinning in the air. And out of the machine, there crawled a woman, with a bundle in her arms. And in the bundle was a baby four weeks old; and when the woman opened up the blanket, the baby just winked at the excited crowd and did not say a word.

There recently happened in Detroit an accident which I did not see, but which my sister wrote me about. As a doctor of that city was parking his machine, he backed into a car behind him and broke the lights. He got out to speak to the owner about it, but the owner was not there. He waited, but the owner did not come. He looked for a policeman, but there was none in sight. Finally he took out his card and wrote on it, " I broke your lights; please send the bill to me at ——," and gave his address.

The next day a man came into his office. " You broke my lights," said the man. " Yes," replied the doctor, " but I am ready to pay for them." " You needn't pay for them," said the other man. " I just came in to shake hands with an honest man." " You're a doctor," he continued. " My daughter needs medical attention." And he ended by taking the doctor home with him in his machine, to see what he could do for his daughter. So ended the accident of the broken lights.

I cannot guarantee that if you break the lights on an automobile and leave your card, as this doctor did, the owner will let you off. Though honesty is the best policy, it does not always pay so well as this. But I can guarantee that whenever you have an accident, and you speak right up about it, and take the square way out, you will have a feeling that will be worth a month's wages to you.

TWO
GIVERS

I read in a paper the other day a statement about two men who had recently died. One was a millionaire. He left his money to build homes for orphans, and he said in his will that no colored children should ever be admitted to any of these. They were for white children alone.

The other man was one by the name of Underwood, who lived at May's Landing, New Jersey. He was not a well-known man. Quite the opposite, in fact. He kept one of those little stores that spring up everywhere near schoolhouses, and he sold candy and pencils and tops and such things to the children. He saved up the pennies he took in and invested them in some land near by.

When he died he didn't have much, compared with the other man. But he did have about one hundred thousand dollars. And he did a curious thing with it. He left it to the school board of his town, to use in any way they wanted to for the benefit of the children. Among these there were half a dozen colored children. All the rest were white. But Mr. Underwood himself was a colored man.

I said he didn't have much, compared with

the first man. That was a mistake. He didn't
have much money, compared to him; but of
sympathy, of the love that takes in all sorts
of people, of real human bigness, he had ten
times as much. A colored man, a little store-
keeper in a little town, he yet drew a bigger
circle around him than this millionaire. Draw
your circle as big as you can.